CW00540881

© 2011 Egmont UK Limited.

Age
6-7
Maths

I Can Learn

Times Tables

Written by David Kirkby

Illustrated by John Haslam

This book belongs to

_____

EGMONT

Tips for happy home learning

Make learning fun by working at your child's pace
and always giving tasks that they can do.
Tasks that are too difficult will discourage them
from trying again.

Give encouragement and praise and remember
to award gold stars and sticker badges for
effort as well as good work.

Always do a little rather than too much,
and finish each session on a positive note.

Don't work when you or your child
is tired or hungry.

Reinforce workbook activities and new ideas
by making use of real objects around the home.

EGMONT
We bring stories to life

First published in Great Britain 2005 by Egmont UK Limited
239 Kensington High Street, London W8 6SA

Published in this edition 2011

Text and illustrations © Egmont UK Limited
All rights reserved.

ISBN 978 1 4052 5921 7
1 3 5 7 9 10 8 6 4 2
Printed in Italy

Write in the missing numbers.

 1 cat 2 ears 1 x 2 = 2

 4 cats ☐ ears ☐ x 2 = ☐

 3 cats ☐ ears ☐ x 2 = ☐

 7 cats ☐ ears ☐ x 2 = ☐

 2 cats ☐ ears ☐ x 2 = ☐

Complete the table.

In	6	2	9	10	5	8	4	1
Out	12							

4 **TWOS**

Complete the number sentences.

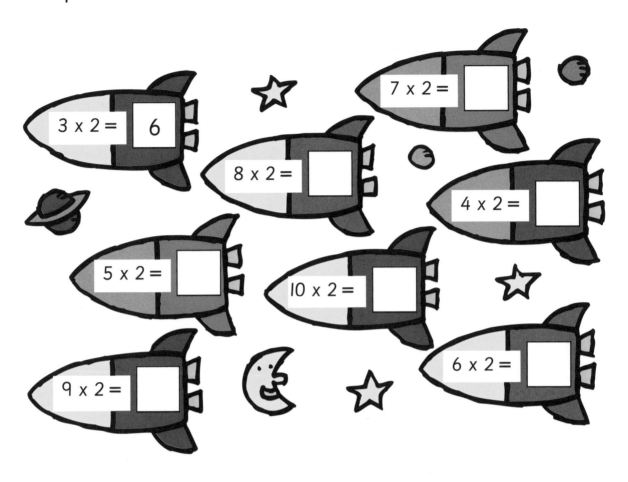

3 x 2 = 6

7 x 2 =

8 x 2 =

4 x 2 =

5 x 2 =

10 x 2 =

9 x 2 =

6 x 2 =

Write numbers in the grid on the right by multiplying by 2.

2	8	6	4
4	3	1	9
7	10	5	6
5	0	7	8

x 2 →

4	16		

Note for parents: Counting everyday objects in pairs, such as socks and shoes, is a fun way to learn the two times table.

Write in the missing numbers.

 3 rows of [4] [4] x 3 = [12]

 3 rows of [ ] [ ] x 3 = [ ]

 3 rows of [ ] [ ] x 3 = [ ]

 3 rows of [ ] [ ] x 3 = [ ]

 3 rows of [ ] [ ] x 3 = [ ]

1 x 3 = 3	2 x 3 =	3 x 3 =	4 x 3 =	5 x 3 =
6 x 3 =	7 x 3 =	8 x 3 =	9 x 3 =	10 x 3 =

Write in the missing numbers.

 1 triangle   3   corners   1 x 3 = 3

 5 triangles   ☐   corners   ☐ x 3 = ☐

 6 triangles   ☐   corners   ☐ x 3 = ☐

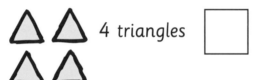 4 triangles   ☐   corners   ☐ x 3 = ☐

 2 triangles   ☐   corners   ☐ x 3 = ☐

Complete the table.

In	6	10	3	7	2	8	5	9
Out	18							

Great counting!

Complete the multiplications.

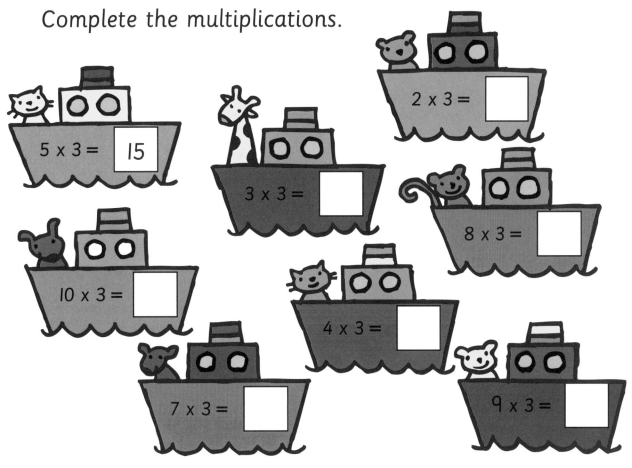

5 x 3 = 15

3 x 3 =

2 x 3 =

8 x 3 =

10 x 3 =

4 x 3 =

7 x 3 =

9 x 3 =

Write numbers in the honeycomb on the right by multiplying by 3.

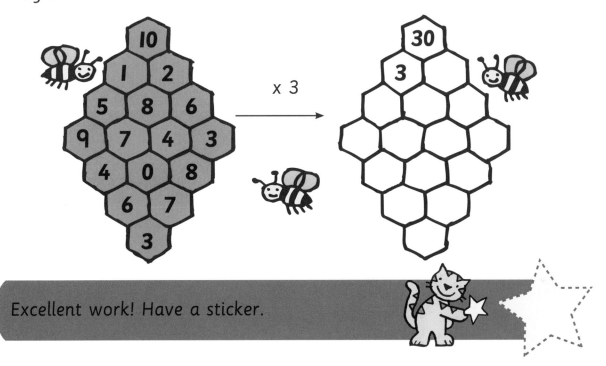

x 3

Fisher

Write in the missing numbers.

4 rows of 5 | 5 x 4 = 20

4 rows of [ ] | [ ] x 4 = [ ]

4 rows of [ ] | [ ] x 4 = [ ]

4 rows of [ ] | [ ] x 4 = [ ]

4 rows of [ ] | [ ] x 4 = [ ]

4 rows of [ ] | [ ] x 4 = [ ]

| 1 x 4 = 4 | 2 x 4 = | 3 x 4 = | 4 x 4 = | 5 x 4 = |
| 6 x 4 = | 7 x 4 = | 8 x 4 = | 9 x 4 = | 10 x 4 = |

 Well done, you're good at this!

Write in the missing numbers.

 1 square | 4 | corners | 1 | x 4 = | 4

 3 squares | ☐ | corners | ☐ | x 4 = | ☐

 7 squares | ☐ | corners | ☐ | x 4 = | ☐

 2 squares | ☐ | corners | ☐ | x 4 = | ☐

 5 squares | ☐ | corners | ☐ | x 4 = | ☐

Complete the table.

In	2	9	7	5	10	4	6	8
Out	8							

Choose a sticker for your hard work.

Complete the number sentences.

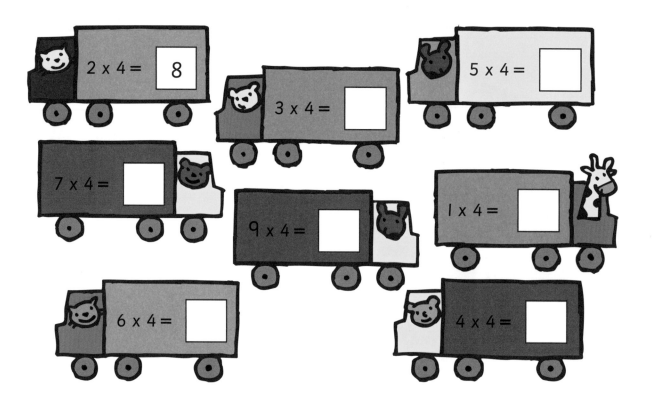

2 x 4 = 8

3 x 4 = ☐

5 x 4 = ☐

7 x 4 = ☐

9 x 4 = ☐

1 x 4 = ☐

6 x 4 = ☐

4 x 4 = ☐

Write numbers in the grid on the right by multiplying by 4.

6	3	10	2
5	1	4	8
4	9	0	3
2	5	6	7

x 4 →

×4

24	12		

 You can do your four times table!

All darts in the ring count double.
Write down the scores for these darts.

scores [6] x 2 = [12]

scores [ ] x 2 = [ ]

scores [ ] x 2 = [ ]

scores [ ] x 2 = [ ]

scores [ ] x 2 = [ ]

scores [ ] x 2 = [ ]

Complete the table.

In	3	5	7	2	8	4	9	6
Out	6							

Super stuff!

Trebling

All darts in the ring count treble.
Write down the scores for these darts.

scores $\boxed{4}$ x 3 = $\boxed{12}$

scores $\boxed{}$ x 3 = $\boxed{}$

scores $\boxed{}$ x 3 = $\boxed{}$

scores $\boxed{}$ x 3 = $\boxed{}$

scores $\boxed{}$ x 3 = $\boxed{}$

scores $\boxed{}$ x 3 = $\boxed{}$

Complete the table.

In	5	8	6	10	4	9	7	3
Out	15							

Note for parents: Remember to encourage and praise your child even if they don't answer all the questions correctly.

Write in the missing numbers.

 5 rows of 5 $\boxed{5}$ x 5 = $\boxed{25}$

 5 rows of ☐ ☐ x 5 = ☐

 5 rows of ☐ ☐ x 5 = ☐

 5 rows of ☐ ☐ x 5 = ☐

 5 rows of ☐ ☐ x 5 = ☐

| 1 x 5 = 5 | 2 x 5 = | 3 x 5 = | 4 x 5 = | 5 x 5 = |
| 6 x 5 = | 7 x 5 = | 8 x 5 = | 9 x 5 = | 10 x 5 = |

Write in the missing numbers.

 1 pentagon [5] sides [1] x 5 = [5]

 3 pentagons [ ] sides [ ] x 5 = [ ]

 6 pentagons [ ] sides [ ] x 5 = [ ]

 5 pentagons [ ] sides [ ] x 5 = [ ]

 2 pentagons [ ] sides [ ] x 5 = [ ]

Complete the table.

In	3	7	4	9	2	8	5	10
Out	15							

Excellent work! Have a star.

Complete the multiplications.

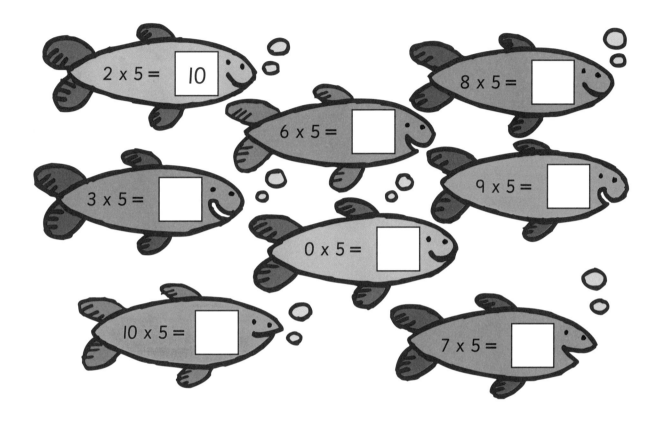

$2 \times 5 = \boxed{10}$

$8 \times 5 = \boxed{}$

$6 \times 5 = \boxed{}$

$3 \times 5 = \boxed{}$

$9 \times 5 = \boxed{}$

$0 \times 5 = \boxed{}$

$10 \times 5 = \boxed{}$

$7 \times 5 = \boxed{}$

Write numbers in the honeycomb on the right by multiplying by 5.

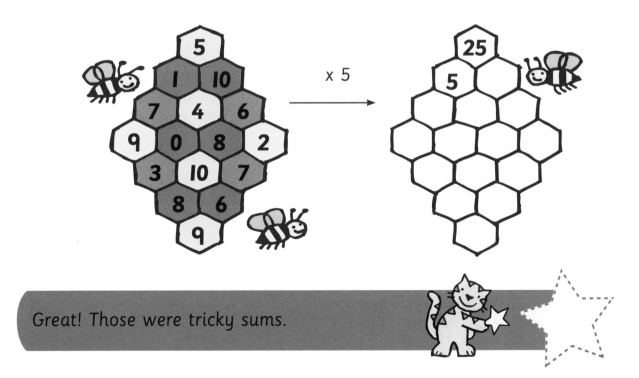

Great! Those were tricky sums.

Sharing between two

Share these shapes between two by drawing them.

| 8 | shared by 2 is | 4 | each | | 8 | ÷ 2 = | 4 |

| ☐ | shared by 2 is | ☐ | each | | ☐ | ÷ 2 = | ☐ |

| ☐ | shared by 2 is | ☐ | each | | ☐ | ÷ 2 = | ☐ |

Complete the table. Say each sum when you write it.

2 ÷ 2 = 1	4 ÷ 2 =	6 ÷ 2 =	8 ÷ 2 =	10 ÷ 2 =
12 ÷ 2 =	14 ÷ 2 =	16 ÷ 2 =	18 ÷ 2 =	20 ÷ 2 =

Note for parents: Introduce your child to the vocabulary associated with division – share, divide and the division sign ÷.

Sharing between three

17

Share these shapes between three by drawing them.

| 6 | shared by 3 is | 2 | each | 6 | ÷ 3 = | 2 |

| | shared by 3 is | | each | | ÷ 3 = | |

| | shared by 3 is | | each | | ÷ 3 = | |

Complete the table. Say each sum when you write it.

3 ÷ 3 = 1	6 ÷ 3 =	9 ÷ 3 =	12 ÷ 3 =	15 ÷ 3 =
18 ÷ 3 =	21 ÷ 3 =	24 ÷ 3 =	27 ÷ 3 =	30 ÷ 3 =

Note for parents: Explain to your child that division is the opposite of multiplication.

These are piles of 2p coins.

Write down how much money there is in each pile.

 5 x 2p = 10p

 [ ] x 2p = [ ]

 [ ] x 2p = [ ]

 [ ] x 2p = [ ]

 [ ] x 2p = [ ]

 [ ] x 2p = [ ]

 [ ] x 2p = [ ]

 [ ] x 2p = [ ]

Complete the table.

1 x 2p =	2 x 2p =	3 x 2p =	4 x 2p =	5 x 2p =
6 x 2p =	7 x 2p =	8 x 2p =	9 x 2p =	10 x 2p =

Note for parents: Try this exercise using real coins; children learn more easily when using real objects.

These are piles of 5p coins.
Write down how much money there is in each pile.

 3 x 5p = 15p

 ☐ x 5p = ☐

 ☐ x 5p = ☐

 ☐ x 5p = ☐

 ☐ x 5p = ☐

 ☐ x 5p = ☐

 ☐ x 5p = ☐

 ☐ x 5p = ☐

Complete the table.

1 x 5p = 5p	2 x 5p =	3 x 5p =	4 x 5p =	5 x 5p =
6 x 5p =	7 x 5p =	8 x 5p =	9 x 5p =	10 x 5p =

You are doing very well.

Write in the missing numbers.

1 tower | 10 | cubes | 1 | x 10 = | 10

4 towers | | cubes | | x 10 = |

3 towers | | cubes | | x 10 = |

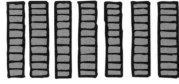

7 towers | | cubes | | x 10 = |

2 towers | | cubes | | x 10 = |

Complete the table.

In	2	5	8	10	9	6	7	4
Out	20							

Was that one easy?

These are piles of 10p coins.
Write down how much money there is in each pile.

 4 x 10p = 40p

 ☐ x 10p = ☐

 ☐ x 10p = ☐

 ☐ x 10p = ☐

 ☐ x 10p = ☐

 ☐ x 10p = ☐

 ☐ x 10p = ☐

 ☐ x 10p = ☐

Complete the table.

| 1 x 10p = 10p | 2 x 10p = | 3 x 10p = | 4 x 10p = | 5 x 10p = |
| 6 x 10p = | 7 x 10p = | 8 x 10p = | 9 x 10p = | 10 x 10p = |

What a lot of money!

Write in the missing numbers.

 1 hexagon $\boxed{6}$ corners $\boxed{6}$ x 6 = $\boxed{6}$

 5 hexagons $\boxed{}$ corners $\boxed{}$ x 6 = $\boxed{}$

 3 hexagons $\boxed{}$ corners $\boxed{}$ x 6 = $\boxed{}$

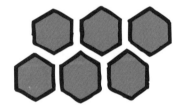 6 hexagons $\boxed{}$ corners $\boxed{}$ x 6 = $\boxed{}$

 2 hexagons $\boxed{}$ corners $\boxed{}$ x 6 = $\boxed{}$

Complete the table.

In	4	6	10	8	3	7	9	5
Out	24							

Let's count corners this time!

Complete these multiplications.

 x 2 = 10   x 6 = ☐   x 2 = ☐

 x 4 = ☐   x 5 = ☐   x 3 = ☐

Draw the missing spots on these dice.

☐ x 3 = 18   ☐ x 4 = 16   ☐ x 2 = 8

☐ x 3 = 15   ☐ x 5 = 25   ☐ x 6 = 36

Dice game for two players.

You need two dice, and a set of counters each. Take turns to throw both dice and multiply the numbers together.

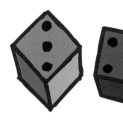

3 x 4 = 12

The player with the larger score takes a counter. The winner is the first to collect 10 counters.

Complete these multiplications.

fives

3 x 5 =	15	5 x 5 =		6 x 5 =	
8 x 5 =		10 x 5 =		9 x 5 =	
4 x 5 =		7 x 5 =		2 x 5 =	

tens

1 x 10 =	10	6 x 10 =		2 x 10 =	
4 x 10 =		0 x 10 =		7 x 10 =	
8 x 10 =		3 x 10 =		5 x 10 =	

sixes

5 x 6 =	30	7 x 6 =		2 x 6 =	
9 x 6 =		4 x 6 =		0 x 6 =	
1 x 6 =		8 x 6 =		3 x 6 =	

 Well done. Choose a big gold star.

Write in the missing numbers.

 1 card [9] spots [1] x 9 = [9]

 3 cards [ ] spots [ ] x 9 = [ ]

 5 cards [ ] spots [ ] x 9 = [ ]

 4 cards [ ] spots [ ] x 9 = [ ]

 2 cards [ ] spots [ ] x 9 = [ ]

Complete the table.

In	3	5	10	7	8	9	6	2
Out	27							

Note for parents: Repeating these types of exercises reinforces essential mental maths skills.

Write in the missing numbers.

 1 pod ☐7☐ peas ☐1☐ x 7 = ☐7☐

 4 pods ☐ peas ☐ x 7 = ☐

 2 pods ☐ peas ☐ x 7 = ☐

 6 pods ☐ peas ☐ x 7 = ☐

 3 pods ☐ peas ☐ x 7 = ☐

Complete the table.

In	3	5	7	4	9	8	10	6
Out	21							

Note for parents: Simply reciting a table does not show understanding of it. Your child could say the table backwards.

Write in the missing numbers.

 1 octopus $\boxed{8}$ legs $\boxed{1}$ x 8 = $\boxed{8}$

 6 octopuses $\boxed{}$ legs $\boxed{}$ x 8 = $\boxed{}$

 3 octopuses $\boxed{}$ legs $\boxed{}$ x 8 = $\boxed{}$

 2 octopuses $\boxed{}$ legs $\boxed{}$ x 8 = $\boxed{}$

 4 octopuses $\boxed{}$ legs $\boxed{}$ x 8 = $\boxed{}$

Complete the table.

In	4	6	9	7	5	10	2	8
Out	32							

Complete these multiplications.

nines

2 x 9 = 18	5 x 9 = ☐	7 x 9 = ☐
6 x 9 = ☐	3 x 9 = ☐	9 x 9 = ☐
8 x 9 = ☐	10 x 9 = ☐	4 x 9 = ☐

eights

3 x 8 = 24	6 x 8 = ☐	5 x 8 = ☐
7 x 8 = ☐	2 x 8 = ☐	10 x 8 = ☐
4 x 8 = ☐	9 x 8 = ☐	8 x 8 = ☐

sevens

1 x 7 = 7	4 x 7 = ☐	6 x 7 = ☐
0 x 7 = ☐	9 x 7 = ☐	3 x 7 = ☐
8 x 7 = ☐	2 x 7 = ☐	7 x 7 = ☐

Note for parents: Remember, each new table only has a few new facts. If you know the 3 times table, you know 6 x 3 and 7 x 3, for example.

Share these shapes between four by drawing them.

8 | shared by 4 is | 2 | each   8 ÷ 4 = 2

[ ] shared by 4 is [ ] each   [ ] ÷ 4 = [ ]

[ ] shared by 4 is [ ] each   [ ] ÷ 4 = [ ]

Complete the table. Say each sum when you write it.

4 ÷ 4 = 1	8 ÷ 4 =	12 ÷ 4 =	16 ÷ 4 =	20 ÷ 4 =
24 ÷ 4 =	28 ÷ 4 =	32 ÷ 4 =	36 ÷ 4 =	40 ÷ 4 =

Note for parents: You could demonstrate the concept of sharing to your child by using sweets or cutting slices from a cake.

Write these multiplications.

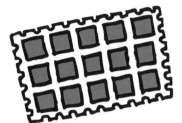

| 3 | x | 5 | = | 15 |

| ☐ | x | ☐ | = | ☐ |

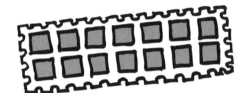

| ☐ | x | ☐ | = | ☐ |

| ☐ | x | ☐ | = | ☐ |

Complete the multiplication tables.

x	3	4	5	6
3	9	12		
4			20	
5				
6		24		

x	2	7	5	9
1		7		
6				
3				27
8		56		

Write these multiplications.

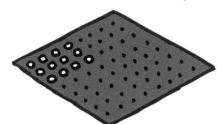

| 3 | x | 4 | = | 12 |

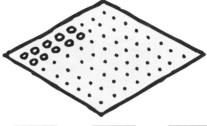

| ☐ | x | ☐ | = | ☐ |

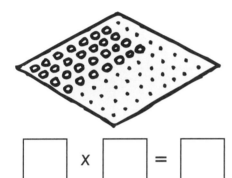

| ☐ | x | ☐ | = | ☐ |

| ☐ | x | ☐ | = | ☐ |

Complete the multiplication tables.

x	5	6	7	8
5		30		
6				48
7				
8				

x	4	7	8	5
9				
6				
3				
10				

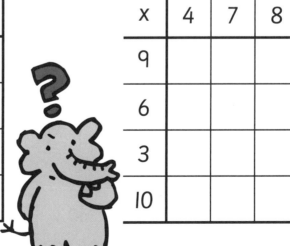

Brilliant again!

Multiplying

Write in the missing numbers.

twos   ☐ x 2 = 6   2 x ☐ = 10   ☐ x 2 = 16

threes   3 x ☐ = 15   ☐ x 3 = 12   3 x ☐ = 30

fours   ☐ x 4 = 24   4 x ☐ = 32   ☐ x 4 = 12

fives   5 x ☐ = 35   ☐ x 5 = 45   5 x ☐ = 10

sixes   ☐ x 6 = 60   6 x ☐ = 30   ☐ x 6 = 6

sevens   7 x ☐ = 0   ☐ x 7 = 63   7 x ☐ = 42

eights   ☐ x 8 = 40   8 x ☐ = 32   ☐ x 8 = 64

nines   9 x ☐ = 27   ☐ x 9 = 81   9 x ☐ = 63

tens   ☐ x 10 = 60   10 x ☐ = 20   ☐ x 10 = 70

You are a superstar!